THIRD
ASSESSMENT PAPERS IN
ENGLISH

JM BOND

Nelson

Underline the right answers.

In its first form, raffia work was simply the interlacing of grasses and rushes, and this was being done many thousands of years ago.

Raffia is a kind of palm tree that grows on the islands round Madagascar. The leaves of this tree grow to nearly fifteen metres in length. The material we know as raffia comes from these leaves. The inner skins of the leaves are peeled and then stretched out in the tropical sun, which dries and bleaches them. The dried raffia is made up into hanks, and sold by weight. Natural raffia is a creamy colour but it can be dyed very easily. If you find the raffia stiff to handle you can soak it for an hour or two in water, and leave it to dry. Raffia can be plaited, twisted, woven, knotted, stitched and embroidered.

1 This passage could be called (Madagascar, Raffia, Crafts)

2 Raffia is made from (palm leaves, rushes, grasses, plaits)

3 To bleach is (to sand, to colour, to wet, to whiten)

4 Which part of the leaf is used to make raffia?
   (The inside, the peel, the outside)

5 How can you soften raffia?
   (By peeling it, by bleaching it, by wetting it)

6–7 Before raffia was used, which two things did the first people use?
   (Plaits, palms, hanks, grasses, rushes)

8 Hanks are (handkerchiefs, loops or coils, weights)

9 Leaves of the raffia palm are (wide, stretched, pointed, long, round)

10–15　Can you arrange the letters in heavy type to form words?

We had a lovely **prupes** .... last night. Mum cooked some

hfsi .... and chips and some **seap** .... Then we had

an **plepa** .... crumble and cream. I was still hungry so I had

some biscuits, **ttubre** .... and **hsceee** ....

Fill in the following group names.

16　A .... of sheep　　17　A .... of bees

18　A .... of monkeys　19　A .... of birds

20　A .... of puppies　21　A .... of fish

22　A .... of geese　　23　A .... of cattle

In each of the following lines underline the word that means the same as the word on the left.

24　**often**　　seldom　　always　　frequently　　never　　sometimes

25　**conceal**　hide　　stick　　show　　confess　　confide

26　**repair**　　break　　repast　　remain　　make　　mend

27　**abandon**　bandage　　leave　　collect　　lose　　find

28　**remote**　surrounding　near　　mean　　distant　　close

Underline the nouns in this passage.

29–36　My aunt and uncle came to stay with us last Wednesday. Next week we are taking them to the theatre to see a pantomime called "Puss in Boots".

Fill in the following spaces with either **to, too** or **two**.

37　There are .... girls here.

38　I will give it .... him.

39　Steven said that Paul and his brother went ....

3

The name of an animal appears in each line. Write the name in the space.

40　You catch balls well.　..

41　He scowled when he couldn't do it.　..

42　He had a red tassel on his cap.　..

43　They trampled all over the garden.　..

44　He threw everything on the floor.　..

45　"Where are you going to advertise it?"　..

Where do the following live ?

46　pig ....　47　vicar ....　48　bird ....

49　Eskimo ....　50　traveller....................　51　bee ....

52　lion ....　53　nun........................　54　monk ....

Put inverted commas (speech marks) in the following passage:

55–62　　I'm not coming back to school any more, said Anne.
　　　Diana gasped and stared at Anne to see if she meant it. Will
　Marilla let you stay at home? she asked.
　　　She'll have to, said Anne. I'll never go to school to that man
　again.
　　　　　　　　From *Anne of Green Gables* by L.M. Montgomery

Put these words in dictionary order.

　flame　　fire　　flood　　first　　flap　　flop

63　(I) ....　64　(2) ....　65　(3) ....

66　(4) ....　67　(5) ....　68　(6) ....

69–74　Some words can be given an opposite meaning by putting the prefix
　　　un or **dis** in front of them. Can you put these words in the right
　　　column?

　selfish　honest　agree　certain　order　common

　　　un　　　　　　　　**dis**

　　　....................　　　....................

　　　....................　　　....................

　　　....................　　　....................

4

In this short rhyme two words are missing. Can you fill them in?

75–76 Girls scream
Boys shout;
Dogs bark

School's ....
Cats run
Horses shy;
Into trees

Birds ....

Complete the following adjectives of comparison.
Example: good   better   best

77–78 rich   ....

79–80 bad   ....

81–82 quiet   ....

83–84 pretty   ....

85–86 many   ....

87–88 early   ....

Write the opposite of the word in heavy type.

89 The sea was very **rough**.   ....

90 She **bought** a book.   ....

91 It was a **dull** day.   ....

92 The dress was **beautiful**.   ....

93 Karen **always** laughs.   ....

94 Mum was very **sad**.   ....

Many things go together, such as **bucket and spade**. Complete the following.

95 Shoes and ....   96 Soap and ....

97 Knife and ....   98 Needle and ....

99 Bread and ....   100 Hat and ....

Underline the right answers.

There is a lake near our town and it is very popular with both adults and children. Many boys and girls have their own sailing boats, which are called "Cadets". The grown-ups have many types of boats, but the most popular are the "Herons" and the "Enterprises". The Sailing Club is at the south end of the lake and at the opposite end is a boathouse where visitors can hire various craft—sailing boats, rowing boats and canoes. Towards the middle of the lake on one side there is a part which is roped off. This is used for swimming. Sometimes a sailing boat capsizes, and as the water is not very deep this can provide much merriment for the onlookers! There are many reasons why a boat may capsize. Usually it is caused by a violent gust of wind, but it may be due to overloading, a faulty boat, or simply lack of skill in handling the craft.

1-3 What kinds of boats are there on the lake?
(Sailing boats, steamers, rowing boats, canoes, cruisers)

4 What is at the south end of the lake?
(The Sailing Club, the boathouse, the swimming area)

5 What is in the middle?
(A place for swimming, the Sailing Club, the boathouse)

6 Name the sailing boats used by children. (Cadets, Herons, Enterprises)

7 If I wanted to hire a boat to which end should I go? (North, south)

8–9   Name the most popular sailing boats used by adults.
(Eagles, Herons, Mustangs, Fireflies, Enterprises, Cadets)

10–13   Underline the reasons why the boats capsize.
(There are too many boats, lack of skill, overloading, lack of paint,
wind, rain, faulty boats)

14–19   Underline the verbs.

As he was late, the boy ran to the station. He hurried on to the
platform and boarded the train a second or two before the guard
waved his flag and the train moved away.

Look at each verb (doing word) on the left, and then see which of the words
in the list on the right of the page best describes it.

20	arrived	....	carefully
21	waited	....	generously
22	slept	....	punctually
23	worked	....	patiently
24	gave	....	soundly

Write one of these four prepositions in each space.

with   over   from   up

25   He ran .... the stairs.

26   The teacher was cross .... the cheeky boy.

27   Your T-shirt is different .... mine.

28   The boy climbed .... the wall.

Give the feminine of the following words.

29	actor	....	30	hero	....
31	master	....	32	man	....
33	uncle	....	34	nephew	....
35	waiter	....	36	bull	....

37 A young sheep is called a ....

38 A young lion is called a ....

39 A young duck is called a ....

40 A young goose is called a ....

41 A young horse is called a ....

42 A young cow is called a ....

43 A young hen is called a ....

44 A young goat is called a ....

Fill in the following spaces with **past** or **passed**.

45 We went .... the gate.

46 We .... the cinema.

47 John .... the book to his sister.

48 The cars flashed ....

49 I crept .... the bedroom door.

50 Tom .... the ball to the goalkeeper.

Underline the word which rhymes with the word on the left.

51 **come**   home   drum   foam   loam

52 **love**   wove   dove   tore   gave

53 **cow**   sew   low   how   mow

54 **guest**   host   worst   most   quest

55 **yolk**   silk   talk   poke   sulk

In each of the following lines there is a word which does not fit in with the rest. Underline that word.

56 glass   table   cup   plate   saucer

57 green   blue   yellow   sky   red

58 pen   pencil   chalk   crayon   book

59 dog   rabbit   hutch   mouse   cat

8

60	fish	pork	mutton	lamb	veal
61	leg	arm	foot	sock	hand
62	ring	watch	ear-ring	bracelet	ribbon
63	window	garden	door	roof	chimney

Write in full the words for which these abbreviations stand.

64 Jan ....

65 M.P. ....

66 G.P.O. ....

67 N.W. ....

68 H.Q. ....

Choose from each bracket the word which will make the statement correct.

69 Wrist is to hand as (toe, ankle, leg) is to foot.

70 House is to man as (barn, shed, sty) is to pig.

71 Sun is to day as (moon, stars, dark) is to night.

72 Foot is to man as (hoof, tusk, paw) is to dog.

73 Bat is to cricket as (paddle, racquet, yacht) is to tennis.

74 Pen is to ink as (brush, pot, box) is to paint.

What do the following expressions mean?

75	black and blue	....	to be polite
76	a white elephant	....	badly bruised
77	to be in hot water	....	smart and clean
78	to mind one's Ps and Qs	....	to make a new start
79	a red letter day	....	something useless
80	spick and span	....	an important day
81	to turn over a new leaf	....	to be in trouble

After each of the following lines write a word that means the same as the word in heavy type.

82 The sailors were told to **abandon** ship. ....

83 The airman received an award for his **heroic** deed. ....

84 I have **sufficient** money to buy it. ....

85 She **inquired** how long she would have to wait. ....

86 The **entire** school went on the outing. ....

87 The children **dispersed** in all directions. ....

88 The soldier **encountered** many difficulties. ....

89–100 See if you can fill in the missing words in this poem.
The chief defect of Kenneth Plumb
Was chewing too much bubble-...................... .
He chewed away with all his......................
Morning, evening, noon and ....
Even, oh! it makes you ....
Blowing bubbles in his sleep.
He simply could not get enough,
His face was covered with the ....
As for his teeth – oh! what a .... ,
It was a wonder he could bite.
His loving mother and his dad
Both remonstrated with the ....
Ken repaid them for the trouble
By blowing yet another ....

Kenneth by Wendy Cope

A defect is a: hobby, fault, game, reflection
Remonstrated means: protested, stated, talked, laughed
His teeth became: white, unwashed, decayed, false
This was because he: was hungry, ate too much sugar, was lonely, could not sleep

Underline the right answers.

Four o'clock strikes,
There's a rising hum,
Then the doors fly open,
The children come.
With a wild cat call
And a hop-scotch hop
And a bouncing ball
And a whirling top.
Grazing of knees,
A hair-pull and a slap,
A hitched-up satchel
A pulled down cap.

Bully boys reeling off,
Hurt ones squealing off,
Aviators wheeling off,
Mousy ones stealing off.
Woollen gloves for chilblains,
Cotton rags for snufflers,
Pig-tails, coat-tails,
Tails of mufflers.
Thinning away now
By some and some.
Thinning away, away.
All gone home.

Four o'clock by Hal Summers

1 The children are coming out of (a shop, a cinema, a school)

2 What time is it? (Four o'clock, nine o'clock, I don't know)

3 What time of the year is it? (Summer, winter, I don't know)

4 "A rising hum" is (the noise coming from a high building, someone humming in a high voice, a noise getting louder)

5 "Cotton rags" are for (people with colds, people who take snuff, people with chilblains)

11

6 "Tails of mufflers" are (tails of pet mice, ends of scarves, tails of pigs)

7 The quiet children are called (the mousy ones, the hurt ones, snufflers, aviators)

8 The cyclists are called (bully boys, aviators, those with pulled down caps)

9 Another word for crying is (whirling, wheeling, squealing, reeling)

10 In the poem, to go off quietly is called (stealing, reeling, thinning, wheeling)

The answers to these clues can be made from letters in the word **sycamore**.

11 alike ....

12 arrived ....

13 container ....

14 a planet ....

Write one word for each definition:

15 Part of a plant that grows downwards and draws food from the soil. ....

16 The time between noon and evening ....

17 A grown-up person ....

18 A member of the army ....

19 A small, white flower which often grows in meadows ....

20 A line of people, one behind another, waiting for their turn to do something. ....

Instead of the word in heavy type, write a word which rhymes with it to make a sensible sentence.

21 In the band he played the **numb** ....

22 He asked **cow** .... he should do it.

23 They climbed on to a **how** .... of the oak tree.

24 She had a nasty **team** .... last night.

25 Dad put a **table** .... on the luggage.

In each of the following lines, underline the word which has an opposite meaning to the word on the left.

26 **good**   unhappy   bad   unpleasant   silly

27 **clean**   dirty   washed   unhealthy   ill

28 **hot**   chilly   windy   cold   warm

29 **winter**   spring   hot   weather   summer

30 **day**   night   evening   noon   dawn

31 **shallow**   fat   lean   deep   swallow

32 **difficult**   impossible   hard   problem   easy

Write each of the following in the past tense.

33 The man catches a fish.   ....

34 Tom begins his homework.   ....

35 Sandra is not well.   ....

36 The children see the circus.   ....

What noises do animals make?

37 A dog ....   38 A bull ....

39 A donkey ....   40 A cat ....

41 A lamb ....   42 A bear ....

43 A monkey ....   44 A lion ....

45 A frog ....

Make adjectives from the following words:

46   friend   a .... girl

47   wood   a .... box

48   winter   a ....scene

49   nature   a .... look

50   tide   a ....wave

51   sense   a .... answer

52   help   a ....nurse

53   music   a .... instrument

In each of the following lines underline the word that does not fit in with the rest.

54   football   cricket   netball   pitch   tennis

55   tights   hair   coat   shoes   hat

56   nose   teeth   nails   toes   wool

57   desk   blackboard   bed   chalk   book

58   plate   cup   saucer   kettle   dish

59   primrose   ash   violet   snowdrop   crocus

Write the words in heavy type in the past tense.

60–61   We **see** .... the paper which the man **holds** ....

62–63   Tom **buys** .... a pen which he **gives** .... to his cousin.

64–65   I **write** .... a letter which my brother **posts** ....

66–67   Andrew **wins** .... the prize which the vicar **presents** ....

68–69   I **walk** .... to school quickly but Jane **catches** ....

me up.

Underline the adjectives.

70–75   The spoiled boy had a red, tearful face as his tired mother said she could not afford the new electric car.

Give the plural of the following words.

76 box .... 77 potato .... 78 tooth ....

79 mouse .... 80 lady .... 81 sheep ....

82 foot .... 83 knife .... 84 woman ....

What would you expect to find

85 in a kettle? ....

86 in a vase? ....

87 in an envelope? ....

88 in a purse? ....

89 in a satchel? ....

90 in a garage? ....

Underline the correct word in brackets.

91–92 The (scent, sent) of the flowers you (scent, sent) me is strong.

93–94 Tom (threw, through) the ball (through, threw) the window.

95–96 The (not, knot) joining these ropes is (not, knot) tied tightly.

97–98 Michelle cut her hand on the (pain, pane) of glass and the (pane, pain) is very bad.

99–100 I saw him (stair, stare) at the man on the (stare, stair).

Underline the right answers.

Finger painting

Collect several small containers, and use one for each colour. Start with white which is the most useful colour and use your largest container for it. Take 6 spoonfuls of paint and mix it with 4 spoonfuls of paste and 4 spoonfuls of water. Mix with a spoon or stick. Remember the paint must be thick. Prepare the other colours in the same way using 3 spoonfuls of paint and 2 spoonfuls each of paste and water.

white + a little dark blue = sky blue	yellow + dark blue = green
white + a little red = pink	red + dark blue = violet
white + a little black = grey	

See what other shades you can make.

1   In finger painting which is the most useful colour?
    (White, black, they are all the same)

2   Stir the mixture with (a knife, your finger, a stick)

3–4   Which two colours make green? (Blue, red, yellow, white)

5   If you wanted a paler green you would add
(water, white paint, blue paint, yellow paint)

6–7   Which two colours make grey? (Black, red, white, blue)

8   If you wanted a darker grey you would add
(black paint, white paint, water)

9   Red and dark blue make (pink, violet, sky blue)

10   Why do they tell you to make more white mixture than other colours?
(Most things are painted white, it is the cheapest paint, it is the
thickest paint, it is used with other colours to make them lighter)

11   What are you told to use for this painting?
(A brush, your fingers, a spoon)

12–19   The words below can be given an opposite meaning by putting either
im or **un** in front of them. Put them in the right columns.

perfect   happy   dressed   pure   kind   possible   patient   sure

     im   **un**

     ....

     ....

     ....

     ....

Write the correct letters in the spaces.

20–21   Elaine was Mrs. Brown's y .... est da .... ter.

22–23   The fr .... dly girl helped the old w .... n across the road.

In each space write the plural of the word on the left.

24   loaf   The lady bought two large ....

25   sheep   The farmer owned a hundred ....

26   baby   The .... were asleep in their prams.

27   goose   The .... waddled across the yard.

28   thief   The .... were caught when they opened the safe.

Write the opposite of each word.

29 asleep ....   30 raise ....   31 careless ....

32 hot ....   33 autumn ....   34 cruel ....

Underline the word which is the same part of speech as the word on the left.

35 **us**   children   came   we   go

36 **kick**   football   goal   play   boys

37 **happy**   dog   friend   him   sad

38 **slowly**   speed   I   come   quickly

39 **man**   he   aunt   strong   go

40 **their**   there   though   our   through

41 **teach**   learn   children   school   books

From the letters in the word DICTIONARY form other words with the following definitions.

42 A metal ....

43 An attack ....

44 A locomotive machine ....

45 A deed ....

46 A measurement ....

47 A record of our day ....

48 Where milk is bottled ....

49 To shed tears ....

Put these towns in alphabetical order.

Norwich   Northwich   Northampton   Nottingham   Norwood   Northallerton

50 (1) ....   51 (2) ....

52 (3) ....   53 (4) ....

54 (5) ....   55 (6) ....

Underline one word in each of the following lines which includes all the others.

56 doll   teddy-bear   toy   ball   bat

57 London   capital   Edinburgh   Paris   Madrid

58 car   vehicle   coach   bus   lorry

59 time   second   hour   minute   day

60 chair   table   sideboard   desk   furniture

61 tennis   football   cricket   game   hockey

62 piano   instrument   drums   guitar   organ

After each of the following lines write a word that means the same as the word in heavy type.

63 I **attempted** to climb the rock.   ....

64 She was **requested** to sit down and wait.   ....

65 He **remarked** that he was cold and tired.   ....

66 The picture **adhered** to the paper.   ....

67 She **frequently** went to see her grandmother.   ....

68 John was **awarded** the first prize.   ....

69 Shaun's family was very **wealthy**.   ....

70 At the concert the children **applauded** loudly.   ....

Underline the pronouns in the following:

71–74 We are going to Hull to see the docks: it should be very interesting.
       We will see several ships, and hope to go round them.

Underline the correct spelling.

75 The (lessen, lesson) started at eleven o'clock.

76 The man gave a (groan, grown) as he lifted his arm.

77 Dad said we must get a new ironing (board, bored).

78 The (loan, lone) sailor had crossed the ocean.

79 The gardener put in (steaks, stakes) for the sweet peas to climb up.

Underline the word in each line which rhymes with the word on the left.

80 **though**   cough   rough   so   thought   bought

81 **alone**   thrown   gone   done   along   only

82 **whole**   while   whale   holly   ghost   goal

83 **move**   love   prove   dove   glove   drove

84 **hour**   pour   hair   floor   power   mower

85 **quay**   play   sway   sea   day   fray

86 **few**   mow   grew   sew   saw   claw

87–95 Fill in the missing words in this poem.
September starts a fresh school .... ,
New pupils feel a twinge of fear.
Our Harvest Festival's displayed,
Our thanks to farmers duly ....
October's damp; the leaves fall ....
We make a book called "Our Home Town".
Big pictures pinned on wall and door;
There's thick mud on the cloakroom ....
November brings us Bonfire ....
With blazing guy and fireworks ....
The Christmas plays – rehearsals .... ,
Who'll sing songs? Who'll speak a part?
December's cold; there's frost and ....
To "Peter Pan" in town we go.
We decorate the school, have treats;
At parties there are prizes, ...

The School Year by Wes Magee

96–100 Look at the words below. Underline any that are spelt wrongly, and write them correctly in the spaces.

receive   beleive   deceive   fourty   ninety

libary   conceit   theif   seize   sheild

....

Paper 5

Underline the right answers.

What is a hobbit? I suppose hobbits need some description nowadays since they have become rare and shy to the Big People, as they call us. They are (or were) a little people, about half our height, and smaller than the bearded Dwarfs. Hobbits have no beards. There is little or no magic about them, except the ordinary everyday sort which helps them to disappear quietly and quickly when large stupid folk like you and me come blundering along, making a noise like elephants which they can hear a mile off. They are inclined to be fat in the stomach; they dress in bright colours (chiefly green and yellow); wear no shoes because their feet grow natural leather soles, and thick warm brown hair like the stuff on their heads (which is curly); have long brown fingers, good natured faces and laugh deep laughs (especially after dinner which they have twice a day when they can get it).

From *The hobbit* by J. R. R. Tolkien

1 What magic can hobbits do? (Make themselves smaller, disappear quickly and quietly, make magic shoes)

2 Hobbits think (elephants, dwarfs, people) make a lot of noise.

3–4 They don't need shoes because (their feet have leathery soles, they don't go out, the hair on their feet keeps them warm, they are too fat)

5–8 Hobbits have (brown hair, bald heads, curly hair, beards, long fingers, pleasant faces)

9 The skin of a hobbit is (white, pink, black, brown, I don't know)

10 Do hobbits enjoy their food? (Yes, no, I don't know)

Form nouns from the words on the left.

11 deep   Before you dive into water you should know its ....

12 wide   The .... of the bath is twenty metres.

13 sell   We bought a washing machine in the ....

14–18   Alter this sentence, putting into direct speech what she actually said.
         Don't forget the punctuation and capital letters!

         She asked him if he had cut the grass.

         ....

If you re-arrange the letters at the end of each line they will give you the
correct word to write in each space.

19 It was a lovely, warm, ... day and I   ynsun

20 was sitting in the .... reading a   aenrdg

21 book. After a time I fell ....   saplee

22 I had an exciting .... in which   madre

23 I found some .... treasure. I   eiddnh

24 was very .... when Mum called me   rrsyo

25 to say it was .... for tea.   mtei

26 Lamb is to sheep as foal is to ....

27 Stand is to sit as up is to ....

28 Finger is to hand as toe is to ....

29 Aunt is to niece as uncle is to ....

30 Open is to shut as clever is to ....

31 Glove is to hand as .... is to foot.

22

Underline the word which is opposite in meaning to the word on the left.

32 **open**   unlatched   closed   ready   wide

33 **false**   fancy   funny   true   teeth

34 **future**   past   present   time   age

35 **seldom**   selfish   always   often   never

36 **expensive**   good   cheap   price   cost

37 **tender**   smart   sender   tough   gentle

38 **forgot**   thought   think   forget   remembered

Fill in the spaces with nouns linked to the words on the left.

39 proud   He took great .... in his new bicycle.

40 invent   His .... became world famous.

41 deep   The man measured the .... of the water.

42 live   The .... of the President was in danger.

43 attend   Her .... at school was very good.

Complete the following table of adjectives of comparison.
Example: good   better   best

44–45	quick	....	....
46–47	plain	....	....
48–49	few	....	....
50–51	old	....	....
52–53	dry	....	....
54–55	small	....	....

Write either **as** or **has** in each space—whichever you think makes sense.

56–57   Tom cannot sing .... he .... a sore throat.

58–59   The girl said that her hands were .... cold .... ice.

60–61   " .... he done .... he was told?"

62–63   " .... she told you that she .... a headache?"

64–65   Joanne ran .... fast .... she could.

23

Complete the following proverbs by choosing a word from the column at the right of the page.

66	A stitch in time saves	fire
67	It is no use crying over spilt	work
68	Where there's a will there's a	speed
69	Two heads are better than	milk
70	Many hands make light	nine
71	More haste less	way
72	Out of the frying pan into the	one

Underline a word in each line which is similar in meaning to the word on the left.

73	**permit**	stop	leave	allow	admit
74	**interior**	outside	inside	back	front
75	**imitate**	copy	like	imagine	draw
76	**expense**	expect	cost	money	charge
77	**pardon**	forget	permit	let	forgive

Give ONE word for each of these definitions:

78   Can be used when eating. It has two, three or four prongs set on the end of a handle.   It is a ....

79   A period of two weeks   It is a ....

80   A network of fine threads spun by a spider to catch insects   It is a ....

81   A big, four-legged animal with tusks, and a long trunk   It is an ....

82   A doll worked by pulling wires or strings in a toy theatre   It is a ....

83   Made by birds as a place in which to lay eggs and bring up their young   It is a ....

84   A raised platform on which plays are often produced   It is a ....

85   Thin rope, line or cord used for tying up parcels   It is ....

Write either **there** or **their** in each of the blanks.

86   I would like to go .... today.

87   .... was someone in the waiting room.

88   I like the colour of .... school uniform.

89   "What a lot of work .... is to do," said Mum.

90–91   The children were told to put .... books inside .... desks.

92   "Stand ....," said the policeman.

93–94   They put .... books over ....

Underline a word in each line which best describes the word on the left.

95   **river**   red   wide   good   useful

96   **sky**   old   nice   stormy   ugly

97   **clock**   alarm   date   warm   bed

98   **kitten**   great   short   long   tiny

99   **boat**   real   motor   simple   bright

100   **fire**   pink   cold   coal   busy

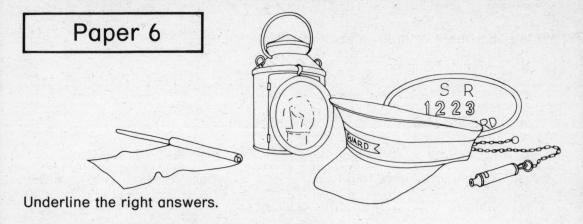

Paper 6

Underline the right answers.

I remember the long homeward ride, begun
By the light that slanted in from the level sun;
And on the far embankment, in sunny heat,
Our whole train's shadow travelling dark and complete.
A farmer snored. Two loud gentlemen spoke
Of the cricket and news. The pink baby awoke
And gurgled awhile. Till slowly out of the day
The last light sank in glimmer and ashy-grey.
I remember it all; and dimly remember, too,
The place where we changed — the dark trains lumbering through;
The refreshment room, the crumbs, and the slopped tea;
And the salt on my face, not of tears, not tears, but the sea.
"Our train at last!" said Father. "Now tumble in!
It's the last lap home!" And I wondered what "lap" could mean;
But the rest is all lost, for a huge drowsiness crept
Like a yawn upon me; I leant against Mother and slept.

Journey home by John Walsh

1 How was I travelling? (In a car, in a train, in a bus)

2–3 The weather was (hot, cold, grey, sunny, stormy)

4–5 In the poem two people slept. They were (the baby, the gentlemen, a farmer, me)

6 Was the baby happy? (Yes, no, I do not know)

7 "The place where we changed." What did we change?
(Seats, clothes, trains, homes)

8 When we waited for the second train we went to
(the refreshment room, the sea, the embankment)

9 Where was I going? (To the seaside, to my home, to a farm)

10 Where do you think I had been? (To school, to see my parents, for a holiday)

11 What time of day was it? (Evening, morning, noon, midnight)

12 "The last lap" means (the person I leant against, a race, the last part of the journey home)

Choose an adverb from the column on the right.

13	In the race the boy ran	suddenly
14	Kim wrote the letter very	neatly
15	The old tramp ate his food	heavily
16	All day the rain fell	soundly
17	The child slept	smartly
18	The car braked	greedily
19	The young lady dressed	swiftly

The noises made by animals are given different names. For example, a dog barks. Write the name given to the noises made by the following animals.

20	a duck	21	turkeys	....
22	a sheep	23	geese	....
24	an elephant	25	a sparrow	....

In each line, underline the correct word in the brackets.

26 On (Teusday, Tuesday, Tusday) I go to the Youth Club.

27 "Pass me a (peace, peice, piece) of bread, please."

28 Of (coarse, course, corse) he can come to tea.

29 Jane (rote, wrought, wrote) an exciting poem.

30 The dog (lay, laid, layed) on the hearth-rug.

31 Pete (through, throw, threw) a cricket ball.

Arrange the following words in dictionary order.

pain   pail   pale   paint   pair   paper

32	(1)	33	(2)	34	(3) ....
35	(4)	36	(5)	37	(6) ....

What do the following expressions mean? Underline the correct answer.

38 hard up (very hard, short of money, at the top)

39 to get into hot water (to get into trouble, to bath, to wash in hot water)

40 to have forty winks (to blink, to play winking, to have a short sleep)

41 to go on all fours (to go to each corner, to ride a horse, to crawl on hands and knees)

42 to play with fire (to ask for trouble, to light fireworks, to put coal on the fire)

43 to play the game (to do P.E., to act fairly, to play when you should work)

44 to lead a dog's life (to live in a kennel, to crawl about, to be treated badly)

Write one word which will describe all the things on each line.
Example: arm   leg   hand   foot   **limbs**

45 socks   vests   blouses   shirts   ....

46 offices   houses   shops   churches   ....

47 franc   cent   penny   dollar   ....

48 beetle   ant   wasp   bee   ....

49 hammer   chisel   spanner   saw   ....

50 ring   watch   necklace   bracelet   ....

In each pair of spaces write two words which sound the same but are spelled differently.
Example: She had to **wait** at the station.
         The **weight** was great.

51–52 She broke a .... of glass.

      She had a .... in her side.

53–54 I brush and comb my ....

      A .... is a small animal.

55–56 He .... where to look for his bat.

      "Look at my .... dress," said Meena.

57–58 I have a .... and an apple.

George has lost a .... of shoes.

Underline the correct word among those in brackets.

59 A kitchen never has   (a sink, a stove, a table, a car)

60 A rose never has   (leaves, knives, buds, a stem)

61 A chair never has   (legs, a back, a clock, a seat)

62 A book never has   (a light, pages, paper, a cover)

63 A bus never has   (a door, seats, legs, a driver)

64–75 In the following passage every sixth word has been left out. Can you fill them in?

Rain and wind, and wind .... rain.

Will the summer come .... ?

Rain on houses, on the .... ,

Wetting all the people's feet.

.... they run with might and .... ,

Rain and wind, and wind .... rain.

Snow and sleet, and .... and snow.

Will the winter .... go?

What do beggar children ....

With no fire to cuddle .... ,

P'raps with nowhere warm to .... ?

Snow and sleet, and sleet .... snow.

Join the two parts of each of the following sentences with one of these words.
    so   but   and   because

76 David likes his tea very hot .... Miranda doesn't like tea at all.

77 I couldn't sing .... I had a sore throat.

78 Kerry has cut her finger .... she will have to bandage it.

79 I am very keen on swimming .... I like diving too.

80 The opposite of **depart** is ....

81 The opposite of **lengthen** is ....

82 The opposite of **buy** is ....

83 The opposite of **find** is ....

84 The opposite of **grow** is ....

85 The opposite of **soften** is ....

Underline the word which rhymes with the word on the left.

86	**buy**	day	bay	tie	toy
87	**lane**	lean	thin	clean	rain
88	**want**	need	don't	font	faint
89	**know**	now	so	how	known
90	**said**	talk	laid	paid	bed
91	**knife**	life	fork	knit	know
92	**voice**	vice	mice	mouse	choice

Underline the correct word in the brackets.

93 None of the girls (were, was) there.

94 Every boy (were, was) on the field.

95 (Their, There, They're) late today.

96 (Were, Where, We're) did you find the book?

97 All the men (were, was) working.

98 You and (me, I) must hurry.

99 I dropped the bag but not one of the eggs (have, has) broken.

100 The boys have (drank, drunk) all the milk.

Underline the right answers.

Not long ago, there lived in London a young married couple of Dalmatian dogs named Pongo and Missis Pongo. (Missis had added Pongo's name to her own on their marriage, but was still called Missis by most people.) They were lucky enough to own a young married couple of humans named Mr. and Mrs. Dearly, who were gentle, obedient, and usually intelligent—almost canine at times. They understood quite a number of barks: the barks for "Out, please!", "In, please!", "Hurry up with my dinner!" and "What about a walk?" And even when they could not understand, they could often guess—if looked at soulfully or scratched by an eager paw. Like many other much-loved humans, they believed that they owned their dogs, instead of realising that their dogs owned them. Pongo and Missis found this touching and amusing and let their pets think it was true.

From *101 Dalmatians* by Dodie Smith

1–2 The dogs' names were (Dalmatian, Pongo, Dearly, Missis)

3–4 Their owners' names were (Mr. Dearly, Mrs. Dearly, Missis, Pongo)

5–7 Their owners (were kind, were old, were slow, did what they were told, were unintelligent, were usually understanding)

8 If the Dearlys didn't understand they (did what they were told, played with the dogs, guessed what they wanted)

9 The dogs had several barks. How many were commands? (1, 2, 3, 4, 5)

10 How many were questions? (1, 2, 3, 4, 5)

11 Pongo and Missis were "touched and amused". Why?
(The Dearlys believed they owned the dogs, they believed that Pongo and Missis owned them, the pets were faithful)

12 "Touched" means (they scratched with their paws, they got a pleasant feeling, they pecked at things)

13 "Canine" means (like a can, like a cat, like a dog)

Underline the correct word in the brackets.

14 They picked some bluebells in a country (lain, lane).

15 Dad told Kevin not to (meddle, medal) with the tools.

16 The class was told to (find, fined) the answer.

17 The cat's (fir, fur) was black and shiny.

18 She found a pretty red (bury, berry) on the tree.

Put a ring round the word which has the same meaning as the word on the left, and underline the word which has the opposite meaning.

19–20	**cease**	stop	crease	continue	go	call
21–22	**alive**	lonely	living	dreary	dead	healthy
23–24	**grief**	sorrow	great	graze	song	joy
25–26	**discovered**	shield	lost	found	cover	place
27–28	**lift**	lower	high	low	stairs	raise

Here are some statements. Some are about elephants and some are about lions. Write **E** after the ones about elephants and **L** after those about lions.

29 They are trained to work in the forests. ....

30 They live in groups called prides. ....

31 The males have manes. ....

32 They have tusks. ....

33 They have golden-brown coats. ....

34 They can push trees down with their trunks. ....

35 They are called the King of Animals. ....

36 They make a trumpetting noise. ....

37 They have a thick grey skin. ....

38 They belong to the cat family. ....

Underline the word which is opposite in meaning to the word on the left.

39 **export**   goods   import   duty   business

40 **sell**   charge   shop   customer   buy

41 **heavy**   light   weight   load   heave

42 **exit**   go   out   excite   entrance

43 **future**   passed   tomorrow   past   evening

Complete the words below by adding either **able** or **ible** to the end.

44 pay ....   45 irrit ....   46 divis ....

47 cap ....   48 invis ....   49 work ....

The answers to the following are all 4-lettered words beginning
with the letter **t**.

50 It grows in gardens
and parks   t ....   51 Not wild   t ....

52 To get exhausted   t ....   53 A story   t ....

54 Ripped   t ....   55 Not false   t ....

56 Toothpaste is often in one t ....

Re-write the following, changing all the underlined words from the singular
to the plural.

57–59 The <u>dwarf</u> ran to <u>his</u> tiny <u>house</u>.

....

60–62 The <u>roof</u> of the <u>factory</u> <u>was</u> red.

....

63–64 The <u>wolf</u> drew near the <u>city</u>.

....

Underline the word in the brackets which means the same as the word in
heavy type.

65 The girl was very **fortunate** to have such a beautiful bicycle.
(Fated, lucky, unlucky, afraid)

66 It was a very **dismal** day. (Dirty, wet, dull, dry)

67 The results of the tests **astonished** everyone.
(Surprised, praised, expected, pleased)

68 The boy was **insolent** to his teacher. (Polite, helpful, kind, rude)

69 The work **commenced** last week. (Finished, started, continued)

In each line, underline a word which is the same part of speech as the word on the left.

70	**toy**	black	little	small	playful	wolf
71	**see**	six	sight	give	day	us
72	**our**	boy	girl	hour	my	hot
73	**happily**	sweet	quickly	sing	laugh	games
74	**good**	girl	hungry	as	book	she

In each line underline a word which means the same as the word on the left.

75	**rapid**	race	slow	quick	crawl
76	**join**	part	unite	joint	crack
77	**govern**	rule	country	nation	cover
78	**quantity**	less	little	amount	more
79	**dusk**	morning	night	sun	twilight
80	**remedy**	pain	cure	remain	illness

Form nouns from the words on the left.

81 sad   There was much .... and suffering.

82 act   His quick .... saved her life.

83 absent   Her .... made things very difficult.

84 angry   The boy's .... was aroused when he saw the dog being ill-treated.

85 fly   The birds prepared for their ....

Underline the correct word in the brackets.

86 Your pencil-box is bigger (than, from, to) mine.

87 Sarah agreed (that, with, to, from) Lisa.

88 Paul's peg is stronger (from, than, to) mine.

89 George's knife is similar (from, to, than) mine.

90 John's coat is different (from, to, than) Pat's.

Put each word on the left into the past tense.

91 shine   Yesterday the sun .... brightly.

92 fight   In 1815, Napoleon .... against the English.

93 sing   We all .... carols last Christmas Eve.

94 dig   The man .... up the lawn and planted some vegetables.

95 eat   We had a lovely picnic and .... lots of sandwiches.

Punctuate the following by putting an apostrophe in each line.

96 "Toms got a new anorak."

97 "Wheres your basket?"

98 "Isnt it there?"

99 "Youll do it soon."

100 "Dont do that!"

Underline the right answers.

     I dared not stir out of my castle for days, lest some savage should capture me. However, I gained a little courage and went with much dread to make sure that the footprint was not my own. I measured my foot against it. Mine was not nearly so large. A stranger, maybe a savage, must have been on shore, and fear again filled my heart.

     I determined now to make my house more secure than ever. I built another wall round it, in which I fixed six guns, so that, if need be, I could fire off six in two minutes. Then I planted young trees around. I feared my goats might be hurt or stolen from me, so I fenced round several plots of ground, as much out of sight as possible, and put some goats in each plot. All this while I lived with a terrible fear in my mind that I might one day meet an enemy. I had lived on this lonely island for eighteen years.

     Once, when on the opposite side of the island, I was filled with horror; for on the ground I saw the remains of a fire, and also a number of human bones. This told me plainly that cannibals had been there.

From *Robinson Crusoe* by Daniel Defoe

1 How did I know the footprint was not mine? (It was smaller than mine, it was larger than mine, it was a strange shape)

2 What did I plant round my house? (A wall, guns, young trees)

3 What did I build round my house? (A fire, a fence, another wall)

4 How did I protect my goats? (By firing guns, by planting trees, by fencing round their plots)

5   What was my greatest fear? (That I might meet an enemy, that I would be burned, that I would be shot)

6   What did I fix to the wall? (Young trees, a chimney, six guns)

7–8   What did I see on the opposite side of the island? (Enemies, cannibals, human bones, savages, the remains of a fire)

9   What told me that cannibals had been on the island? (The sight of human bones, a footprint, a fire)

10   How long had I been on the island? (A few days, eighteen years, I don't know)

Choose the most suitable word from the column on the right to write in each space.

11	The .... of the wind	rustling
12	The .... of thunder	clanking
13	The .... of feet	lapping
14	The .... of the waves	howling
15	The .... of chains	shuffling
16	The .... of leaves	rumbling

17–22   Underline the adjectives (describing words) which are in the following sentence:

The beautiful, young queen took her golden scissors and cut a piece of coloured material, and made a pretty, little bag for the princess.

23–27   Underline the adverbs in the following.

The old lady walked slowly up the hill. She met a small boy who was singing happily as he cycled quickly to school. In the sweetshop the man spoke crossly to the girl who was leaning lazily against the counter.

Underline the correct answers.

28 **Ship-shape** means
(shaped like a boat, seaworthy, neat and tidy)

29 **To make believe** means
(to pretend, to understand, to pray, to tell)

30 **A wet blanket** means
(damp bedclothes, a miserable person, low clouds)

31 **Under the weather** means
(walking in the rain, carrying an umbrella, not feeling well)

32 **Fit as a fiddle** means
(playing a violin, healthy, musical)

33 **Look before you leap** means
(to jump over puddles, to think before you act, to be good at long jumping)

Underline the word which is opposite in meaning to the word on the left.

34 **polite**   pleasant   thankful   rude   police

35 **guilty**   innocent   bad   dirty   happy

36 **stationary**   paper   moving   still   quiet

37 **plenty**   much   more   some   scarce

38 **strong**   heavy   weak   little   fat

39 **expand**   contract   enlarge   small   size

40 **future**   present   happening   past   event

Write the past tense of each word on the left.

41 speak   We .... to her about it.

42 hide   John .... the thimble under the cushion.

43 write   Sharon .... all her party invitations.

44 catch   Daniel .... measles, and David did too.

45 shake   They .... with fright.

46 sing   Thomas .... a solo at the concert.

Squirrels are found in most countries. In Europe it is the red squirrel that is seen most, but in Britain the grey squirrel has been introduced from America. Flying squirrels do not really fly but glide from one tree to another. Ground squirrels may dig large numbers of burrows, and these make "a town".

47–51 Underline the statements below which are true.

There are only grey squirrels in Britain.
Flying squirrels glide.
Grey squirrels first came from America.
Squirrels are only found in Europe.
There are not many squirrels now.
A squirrel's home is called a burrow.
Flying squirrels live in America only.
Many burrows make a town.
The most common squirrel in Europe is the red squirrel.

Some colours have been left out of the following verse. Each colour is mentioned twice. Can you fill them in?

52–63 What is pink? A rose is pink
By the fountain's brink.

What is .... ? A poppy's ....
In its barley bed.

What is .... ? The sky is ....
Where the clouds float through.

What is .... ? A swan is ....
Sailing in the light.

What is .... ? Pears are ....
Rich and ripe and mellow.

What is .... ? The grass is ....
With small flowers in between.

What is .... ? Why, an ....
Just an orange.

Underline the correct word in brackets.

64 Each of the children (have, has) a pencil.

65 None of the girls (were, was) present.

66 All the boys (were, was) early.

67 Neither of the goalkeepers (were, was) hurt.

68 Most of the boys (have, has) a bicycle.

In each space, write an adjective related to the word on the left.

69 patience .... 70 silence ....

71 strength .... 72 friend ....

73 kindness .... 74 heat ....

75 crowd ....

Use a word from the column on the right to fill each space.

76 A breath of .... water

77 A blade of .... grass

78 A pinch of .... salt

79 A pat of .... butter

80 A drop of .... sand

81 A grain of .... air

Underline two words in each line which have something in common with the word on the left.

82–83	**bed**	mattress	dress	sheet	window
84–85	**book**	page	parcel	price	chapter
86–87	**kitchen**	bed	sink	oven	tidy
88–89	**car**	useful	engine	large	brakes
90–91	**Christmas**	room	carols	cards	spring
92–93	**day**	work	morning	lazy	afternoon
94–95	**bicycle**	clothes	hammer	pedals	wheels

40

Underline the conjunctions, or joining words.

96   I am going home soon but he is going to stay here.

97   The dog has a collar and a lead.

98   They waited until the train arrived.

99   Marion was going to school when I saw her.

100 David knew John was there because he had seen him.

Paper 9

Underline the right answers.

Many animals are camouflaged by being the same colour as the places where they live. The polar bear who lives in the snowy far north has white fur. The kangaroo, who lives in dry, dusty grassland, has sandy-coloured fur. The colour of the lion blends in with the colour of dried up grass found in hot countries. The tapirs, who live in the jungles, have a colour pattern which seems of little use – the front of their bodies, their heads and their legs are black, while the rest is white. We can pick out tapirs easily at the zoo but in their homeland it is not so. They hunt at night when there are patches of moonlight and patches of shadow and this is how they are protected. Some animals, like the Arctic fox, who live in cold countries change the colour of their coats in winter so that the new white coat will tone in with the snow. Other animals have a dazzle pattern. A zebra's black and white stripes don't blend in with its surroundings, but zebras feed in the early morning and late evening when they cannot be seen so well. Their outline is broken up against the tall grasses and trees and they become almost invisible.

1 Camouflage is (a background, a disguise, a colour)

2–3 A kangaroo (has a coat which blends in with dried up grass, lives in the desert, has a sand-coloured coat, lives in the jungle)

4 The coat of which animal changes colour in winter? (Bear, zebra, tapir, fox)

5–7 A tapir (lives in the jungle, hunts during the day, is striped, is half black and half white, hunts late)

8 The (fox, zebra, tapir, kangaroo, lion) has a dazzle pattern.

9 Which animal lives in a hot country and has a coat the colour of dried up grass? (Lion, tiger, tapir)

10-11 Which animals are black and white? (Lion, zebra, fox, kangaroo, tapir)

12 Why don't farmyard animals and pets have to have a camouflage? Because (our weather is always changing, they don't have to hide, we are too close to them)

Form nouns linked with the words on the left.

13 think   It was a kind ....

14 visit   The .... was shown round the school.

15 enter   The .... is on High Street.

16 sit   The .... was very comfortable.

17 amuse   The clown caused much ....

Underline one word in each line which does not fit in with the others.

18 snow   frost   hail   sun   ice

19 brave   noble   courageous   good   weak

20 boat   ball   ship   yacht   canoe

21 rope   cord   needle   twine   string

In the first column write a word which means the same as the word on the left. In the second column write a word which means the opposite.

		1st column	2nd column
22-23	difficult	....	....
24-25	interior	....	....
26-27	stern	....	....
28-29	reveal	....	....
30-31	prohibit	....	....

Can you complete the following five-letter words with the following definitions? They all begin with the letters CR.

32 CR .... a lot of people

33 CR .... the Queen sometimes wears one

34 CR .... the noise made by frogs

35 CR .... to fall with a loud noise

36 CR .... a stick with a hooked top used by shepherds

37 CR .... a wading bird; a machine for lifting heavy weights

38 CR .... a thin slice of potato

Look at these pairs of words. If they are alike in meaning write an A. If they are opposite, write an O.

39 author, reader ....

40 fault, error ....

41 here, there ....

42 win, lose ....

43 confess, admit ....

44 gap, hole ....

45 kind, cruel ....

46 teacher, pupil ....

47 eager, keen ....

48 question, answer ....

Complete each line with a word linked to the one on the left.

49 tell   It was an exciting story he ....

50 fell   The .... of snow was very heavy.

51 begin   The .... of the book was not interesting.

52 enjoy   It was worth making the effort to see their ....

Underline the correct word in brackets.

53 They (drank, drunk) their milk.

54 She cannot do (no, any) more.

55 Mr. Scott gave it to Tim and (I, me).

56–57 Neither Vicky (or, nor) Paul (has, have) a book.

58 None of the children (is, are) ready.

44

Complete each sentence by choosing a group of words from the following.

> rough and ready   head and shoulders
> wear and tear   odds and ends

59 Jane's winter coat was showing signs of ....

60 There were lots of .... at the Jumble Sale.

61 Dean was .... taller than Christopher.

62 The repair looked very ....

63–67 Choose the most suitable of these words to fill in each of the blanks in the passage below.

> arrived   accepted   performance   invitation   pleasure

I was very glad to receive an .... to the school concert, and I .... it with .... When I .... at the hall it was nearly time for the .... to begin.

68–73 Give the opposites of the following words by adding **dis** or **un** at the beginning.

lock   ....   wise   ....

obey   ....   safe   ....

appear ....

trust   ....

Underline the opposite of the word on the left.

74 **give**   lend   take   spend   have

75 **sink**   kitchen   drown   rise   lower

76 **finish**   end   find   dish   start

77 **junior**   senior   school   child   boy

78 **wild**   animal   fierce   tame   zoo

79–82 Underline the words which should start with a capital letter.

matthew and his mother went into the countdown supermarket to buy a packet of chockomix.

The names of some objects are shortened in everyday speech. What are the full names of the following?

83 photo .... 84 phone ....

85 exam .... 86 T.V. ....

In each line there are two words which can be abbreviated.
Example: I am going to school. The **I am** can be written **I'm**.

87 We thought we would go to Chester. ....

88 "What I have got I intend to keep." ....

89 I wonder what he will do when he starts work. ....

90 "It does not make sense to me," said Miss Jones. ....

91 "Will the person who is making that noise stand up!" ....

92 "Look! They have escaped at last." ....

93 He will not stop teasing me. ....

94 We are going to arrest that man. ....

Here are some more pairs of words. Can you fit them into the sentences?

hand and foot   fits and starts   slow and sure   bits and pieces
sixes and sevens   ways and means

95 She took all her .... and went to London.

96 They found the .... to raise the money.

97 The old lady never went out. She seemed to be

    bound .... to her work.

98 After the burglars had left the room it was all at ....

99 Anna could have done better. She only worked by ....

100 Tom worked well as he was ....

Paper 10

Underline the right answers.

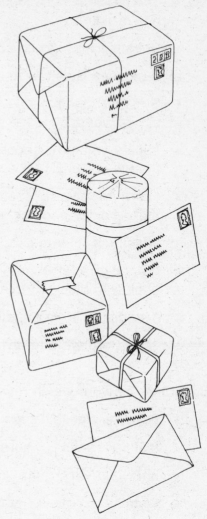

This is the Night Mail crossing the Border,
Bringing the cheque and the postal order.

Letters for the rich, letters for the poor,
The shop at the corner, the girl next door.

Pulling up Beattock, a steady climb:
The gradient's against her, but she's on time.

Past cotton-grass and moorland boulder,
Shovelling white steam over her shoulder,

Snorting noisily, she passes
Silent miles of wind-bent grasses.

Birds turn their heads as she approaches,
Stare from bushes at her blank-faced coaches.

Sheep-dogs cannot turn her course;
They slumber on with paws across.

In the farm she passes no one wakes,
But a jug in a bedroom gently shakes.

Dawn freshens. Her climb is done.
Down towards Glasgow she descends,
Towards the steam tugs yelping down a glade of cranes,
Towards the fields of apparatus, the furnaces
Set on the dark plain like gigantic chessmen.
All Scotland waits for her:
In dark glens, beside pale-green lochs,
Men long for news.

The Night Mail by W. H. Auden

1   Beattock is (a town, a hill, a shop)

2   Why don't the people at the farm wake up? (They don't hear the train,
they are too far away, they are used to the train)

3   The jug shakes because (someone is using it, the train makes it vibrate, it is broken)

4   Does the train go up or down into Glasgow? (Up, down)

5   It reaches Glasgow in (the night, the day, the dawn, the evening)

6   Birds turn their heads (to see what is making the noise, because they are nervous, because they have stiff necks)

7   "She's on time" means (she has an alarm, she is not late, she has time to wake up)

8   "Turn her course" means (stop her, send her back again, make her go another way)

9   Which pronoun is used to describe the train? (She, it, they, he)

10 "Blank-faced coaches" are (ones with no lights, ones painted black, ones with black curtains)

11 "Gradient" is (grain, slope, weight, height)

12 "The Border" is (a division, an edging, a boulder)

Underline the word which rhymes with the one on the left.

13 **haze**   tease   praise   face   grace   waist

14 **foul**   soul   hole   bowl   howl   hen

15 **bite**   wit   hit   fit   lit   sight

16 **comb**   come   hum   home   brush   tomb

17 **wise**   prize   lost   mice   piece   was

Write a word which means the same as the word in heavy type.

18 The house had been **vacant** for some time.   ....

19 It was **suspended** from the ceiling.   ....

20 The girl was very **conceited**.   ....

21 Michael had **completed** his work.   ....

22 He treated the horse very **brutally**.   ....

23 She **comprehended** what the man said.   ....

48

Give the feminine of:

24 gander   ....   25 prince   ....

26 uncle   ....   27 landlord   ....

28 manager   ....   29 drake   ....

Write one word to complete each sentence.

30 Eye is to seeing as ear is to ....

31 Cuckoo is to bird as cat is to ....

32 Sugar is to grocer as meat is to ....

33 Egg is to Easter as mince pie is to ....

34 Fin is to fish as wing is to ....

Complete the following sentences with a word linked with the word on the left.

35 good   Sally was the .... writer in the class.

36 length   Tim has a .... stick than Kim.

37 fast   I can go .... than you.

38 bad   Miss Smith told Tara that her work was the .... in the class.

39 more   Anna had collected the .... pictures.

Complete the following sentences, using the words listed below.

between   since   although   under   until   off   behind

40 .... I waved to her, she didn't see me.

41 .... I have been at this school I have learned to swim.

42 I cannot reach my books .... you have moved that parcel.

43 There is a wall .... the two gardens.

44 You must always sweep .... the mats.

45 The little girl ran .... the path.

46 The boy walked .... the cart.

Underline the word which does not fit in with the others.

47   thimble   needle   pin   plate   scissors

48   mound   saucer   hill   hillock   mountain

49   month   day   May   week   year

50   happy   merry   glad   pleased   cross

51   rubber   candle   light   torch   flame

52   fry   beat   heat   cook   boil

53   chair   bench   table   seat   settee

Underline the correct word or words in the brackets.

54   To exhibit is to (grow, display, exit, linger)

55   To invert means to (reverse, dress, interfere, climb)

56   To resemble is (to murmur, to resign, to be like. to assemble)

57   To surrender is (to suggest, to take, to come, to yield)

58   To maintain is (to climb, to master, to keep, to lose)

Choose a word from the list on the right to fill each space. The idea is to make a new, long word.
Example: snow drop snowdrop

59 tea	60 cup	coat father
61 pen	62 grand	paste table
63 pillow	64 over	knife spoon
65 tooth	66 time	board case

Underline the word which does not fit in with the other words in the line.

67   cup   saucer   cupboard   dish   plate

68   green   blue   pink   cloud   red

69   robin   lion   thrush   sparrow   wren

70   snow   ice   hail   frost   house

71   sing   walk   jump   run   kick

72   Tom   Dick   Jane   Harry   Bill

Complete each sentence with one of the following words.

> sheet   feather   punch   hills   rock   cucumber

73   She was as pleased as .... when she passed her exam.

74   The book looked as old as the ....

75   Even though it was a competition she was as cool as a ....

76   Dad said that the wall was as steady as a ....

77   When Keith got up he looked as white as a ....

78   The baby was as light as a ....

Form adjectives linked with the words on the left.

79   sun   All the children liked the .... classroom.

80   value   They had a .... clock in the hall

81   wood   The .... spoon was used for cake-making.

82   gold   They made a .... crown for the King.

83   beauty   The .... lady presented the prizes.

84   move   They went up on the .... staircase.

REQUIRED IMMEDIATELY
A boy or girl to deliver newspapers.
Hours 6.30 a.m. to 8 a.m. Mondays to Saturdays.
Wages £2 per day. It would be an advantage
if the applicant had a bicycle.
Write to Mr. Jones, Newsagent,
Pensby Road, Moreton.

85–90   Underline the statements that are correct.

The boy or girl must have a bicycle.

He/She would be needed six days a week.

Mr. Jones wants a newsboy or girl quickly.

There is no hurry to reply.

The boy/girl would get paid £4 a week.

He/She would work nine hours a week.

The boy/girl must go to see Mr. Jones.

Mr. Jones doesn't mind if he employs a girl or a boy.

The pay would be £12 a week.

It would be a help if the girl/boy had a bicycle.

On Monday icy rains poured down
and flooded drains all over town.
Tuesday's gales bashed elm and ash;
dead branches came down with a crash.
On Wednesday bursts of hail and sleet,
no-one walked along the street.
Thursday stood out clear and calm
but the sun was paler than my arm.
Friday's frost that bit your ears
was cold enough to freeze your tears.
Saturday's sky was ghostly grey;
we smashed ice on the lake today.
Christmas Eve was Sunday ... and
snow fell and fell across the land.

A Week of Winter Weather Wes Magee

91–92   On which days was it frosty?   ....

93–94   It snowed on .... It rained on ....

95–96   It was very windy on .... When was there flooding? ....

97–98   It hailed on .... Christmas Day was on ....

99   People stayed indoors on ....

100   We are told that there was no wind on ....

Underline the right answers.

There is an old legend about Delhi (the capital of India). Long ago an old Hindu king was hammering a large iron nail into the earth, and as he swung with all his might the tip of the nail struck the head of the snake-god who supports the world on his coiled body. The king trembled at the thought of the snake-god's anger—would he bring fire and plague to his subjects, or even destroy the world? He ordered all his subjects to offer prayers and sacrifices to placate the snake-god. Several months passed and when the god's anger was soothed he told the king that he wouldn't punish him, but he said that on that spot there would always be war and unrest. The iron nail in this fable is supposed to be the Iron Pillar which today stands in the courtyard of a tower built about six hundred years ago. There is another legend which says that if you stand with your back to this pillar and can stretch your arms behind you round the pillar all your wishes will come true. I have watched many people try to do this but no one has had arms long enough to get more than half way round the pillar!

1   A legend is (something that happened a long time ago, something that happened in Bible times, a story, a true story)

2   "With all his might" means that (he used all his strength, he swung round, he fell over)

3   "Coiled" means (made of rope, curled round and round, put in a basket)

4–6 The king was frightened that the god would
(bring war, destroy the earth, make people dreadfully ill, flood
the earth, cause terrible fires)

7 To "placate" means (to put in place, to punish, to please)

8 The king's subjects were (words, people, thoughts, towns)

9–10 The king told his people (to say prayers, to tremble,
to make sacrifices, to fight)

11 Did the god punish the king and his people?
(Yes, no, I don't know, yes, in a way they did not expect)

12 Nowadays, do people find it easy to put their arms round the pillar?
(Yes, no, I don't know)

What jobs do these people have? Underline the most suitable word under
each description.

13 He has a tanned, freckled face. He is wearing an old jacket and
warm, heavy trousers which are stuck into green wellies; these are
caked with mud. He carries a stick.
He is a   doctor,   farmer,   office worker,   steeplejack

14 He wears a pin-striped suit, a white shirt and a grey tie. His shoes
are brightly polished, and he carries a briefcase.
He is a   bus-driver,   a fisherman,   a soldier,   a solicitor

15 She wears a crisp, white overall, and a stethoscope.
She is a   doctor,   groom,   taxi-driver,   builder

16 He wears old trousers, a tee-shirt, a helmet and protective shoes.
He is a   builder,   typist,   cobbler,   golf caddie

Underline one word in the brackets which is connected with the words on the
left.

17 shoe   boot   sandal   (dress   slipper   hat   tea)

18 haddock   sole   cod   (ear-ring   match   hair   herring)

19 head   arm   leg   (glove   coat   sock   foot)

20 coach   car   train   (coat   bus   wait   run)

21 turnip   swede   potato   (garden   fruit   carrot   winter)

22 cup   glass   mug   (beaker   bread   water   china)

Write the opposite of the word in heavy type.

23 One puppy is **asleep**, but the other is ....

24 This material is **coarse**, but yours is ....

25 It is **dangerous** to swim here but over there it is ....

26 David is **generous** but his brother is ....

27 "Don't **frown**! You look much nicer when you ...."

Choose the most suitable word from the column on the right to fill each space.

28 The .... of a drum   tick

29 The .... of coins   chattering

30 The .... of monkeys   jingle

31 The .... of a whip   crack

32 The .... of a clock   beat

Choose one of the adverbs listed on the right to complete each sentence.

33 She acted .... in the emergency.   generously

34 They waited .... at the hospital.   desperately

35 The prisoner fought .... for his life.   loudly

36 The postman knocked .... on the door.   quickly

37 The farmer rose .... in the morning.   anxiously

38 The lady gave .... to the collection.   early

Underline the correct word in the brackets.

39 Uncle Martin is (learning, teaching) me to ride my bicycle.

40 Though Steven ran to the station he (missed, mist) his train.

41 Nobody has (never, ever) jumped that height before.

42 Anybody (is, are) allowed to go in.

43 The girl hasn't (nothing, anything) to do.

44 Both the boys (was, were) fighting.

Arrange the following words in dictionary order.

stilts   ship   seven   stick   shave   shape

45 (I) ....   46 (2) ....   47 (3) ....

48 (4) ....   49 (5) ....   50 (6) ....

Write one word which means the same as the words in heavy type.

51 The man was **on time** for his appointment. ....

52 As we were in a hurry we **kept out of the way of** the crowds. ....

53 Justin's writing was poor, but now it is **getting better**. ....

54 The **well-known** film star was surrounded by crowds of people. ....

Underline one word in each line which does not agree with the rest.

55 hold   maintain   keep   destroy   retain

56 beautiful   nasty   lovely   pretty   handsome

57 happy   unwell   sick   ill   unhealthy

58 write   draw   scribble   paint   kick

59 wall   barrier   house   fence   hedge

60 gigantic   enormous   big   tiny   large

Look at these pairs of words. If they are alike in meaning write an A. If they are opposite write an O.

61 injure   harm   ....

62 girl   boy   ....

63 praise   blame   ....

64 value   worth   ....

65 entire   part   ....

66 choose   select   ....

67 silent   speechless   ....

68 even   odd   ....

Underline the word which has an opposite meaning to the word on the left.

69 **noise**   talk   shout   silence

70 **loose**   lose   soft   cover   tight

71 **sweet**   toffee   drop   sour   sugar

72 **some**   lots   none   more

73 **tall**   high   big   short

Make adjectives linked with the words on the left.

74 music   We had a .... evening at school last week.

75 nation   The dancers wore .... costumes.

76 centre   We went to the .... car park.

77 fashion   The model wore a very .... dress.

78 colour   Her coat was very ....

79 misery   He felt .... at home by himself.

Instead of writing **the towns of Africa** you could write **African towns**.
Do the same below.

80 The people of Wales are the .... people.

81 The rivers of Germany are .... rivers.

82 The castles of Spain are .... castles.

83 The lakes of Ireland are .... lakes.

84 The people of the West Indies are the .... people.

85 The cooking of Pakistan is .... cooking.

In each line two words are abbreviated. Write them in full in the spaces.

86 They'll have to hurry up.   ....

87 He can't remember it now.   ....

88 She wants to know if you're going.   ....

89 He's only got one pair of shoes.   ....

90 Let's go to the disco.   ....

91–100 In this poem, ten words are left out. See if you can fill them in.

Oh, I wish I'd looked .... me teeth,

And spotted the perils beneath,

All the toffees I ....

And the sweet, sticky food,

.... , I wish I'd looked after .... teeth.

I wish I'd been .... much more willin'

When I .... more tooth there .... fillin'

.... pass up gobstoppers

From respect .... me choppers,

And to buy .... else with me shillin'.

Pam Ayres

Paper 12

Underline the right answers.

First came ten soldiers carrying clubs; these were all shaped like the three gardeners, oblong and flat, with their hands and feet at the corners: next the ten courtiers; these were ornamented all over with diamonds, and walked two and two, as the soldiers did. After these came the royal children; there were ten of them, and the little dears came jumping merrily along hand in hand, in couples; they were all ornamented with hearts. Next came the guests, mostly Kings and Queens, and among them Alice recognised the White Rabbit: it was talking in a hurried, nervous manner, smiling at everything that was said, and went by without noticing her. Then followed the Knave of Hearts, carrying the King's crown on a crimson velvet cushion; and, last of all this grand procession, came The King and Queen of Hearts.

From *Alice in Wonderland* by Lewis Carroll

1   Who led the procession? (The gardeners, the soldiers, the White Rabbit)

2   Who were jumping merrily along hand in hand? (The royal children, the King and Queen, rabbits)

3   Which guest did Alice recognise? (The gardener, the White Rabbit, the Knave of Hearts)

4   Who were ornamented all over with diamonds? (The soldiers, the courtiers, the King and Queen of Hearts)

5   Who was carrying the King's crown? (Alice, the Knave of Hearts, the White Rabbit)

6   Who were ornamented with hearts? (The guests, the courtiers, the royal children)

7–8   Who were the most important people in the procession? (Alice, the King of Hearts, the White Rabbit, the Queen of Hearts)

9   How many royal children were there? (Two, I don't know, ten)

10   Who didn't notice Alice?
     (The soldiers, the courtiers, the White Rabbit, the gardeners)

11   What were the soldiers carrying? (Diamonds, hearts, spades, clubs)

12   Which group was fourth in the procession?
     (The soldiers, the guests, the royal children, the gardeners)

Write one word which has the same meaning as the words in heavy type.

13   Marilyn has learnt to skate **with ease.**   ....

14   We are **not allowed** to run on the grass.   ....

15   The naughty boy **was sorry for** what he had done.   ....

16   At one o'clock I feel **the need for food.**   ....

Some words sound the same but are spelled differently. Can you underline the right one in the brackets?

17   They set up their deck-chairs on the (beach, beech)

18   There is a (beach, beech) tree in the garden.

19   (Our, hour) television is broken.

20   It takes me one (our, hour) to get to school.

21   Sam (led, lead) the way to the toy counter.

22   (Led, lead) is a metal.

Underline the correct word inside the brackets.

23   They have (sang, sung, singed) in the choir.

24   We have (run, ran, runned) all the way.

25   He has (fell, fall, fallen) down the steps.

26   She was (laying, lying, laid) on the bed.

27   He had (ate, eaten, ate) all the apples.

28   We have (spoke, speak, spoken) to her about it.

Underline the word which best describes the word on the left.

29   **lesson**   famous   interesting   large   ready

30   **train**   good   fare   fair   express

31	**climate**	lazy	small	warm	late
32	**colour**	bright	wet	painted	cloudy
33	**water**	wet	dry	dusty	hot
34	**fireman**	cold	brave	dark	stormy

Choose a word from the list on the right to fill each space, making a new, longer word.

35	tooth	36	flower	yard	ball
37	foot	38	book	tray	ache
39	church	40	ash	case	pot

Underline the word which is the same part of speech as the word on the left.

41	**me**	girl	boy	am	fat	them
42	**quickly**	lean	slowly	she	speed	was
43	**lovely**	girl	she	is	how	warm
44	**ate**	food	drank	man	he	bread
45	**teacher**	baby	he	taught	me	us
46	**and**	hand	more	me	but	add

Underline the word which rhymes with the word on the left.

47	**ewe**	were	sew	few	throw
48	**word**	lord	board	sword	heard
49	**sole**	foal	alone	gone	sell
50	**chair**	gear	mare	seat	year
51	**pear**	dear	far	jar	dare

Underline the word which has an opposite meaning to the word on the left.

52	**narrow**	long	short	wide	near
53	**finish**	conclude	complain	end	start
54	**shallow**	deep	low	under	allow

55	**hinder**	stop	help	back	under
56	**gentle**	good	kind	rough	man
57	**go**	went	back	forward	come
58	**borrow**	spend	take	lend	sorrow

Underline the word which means the same as the word on the left.

59	**halt**	go	stop	come	red
60	**distress**	mistress	distant	misery	far
61	**timid**	shy	proud	sad	good
62	**guard**	train	hard	govern	protect
63	**observe**	desert	watch	leave	object
64	**rich**	poor	happy	wealthy	sad

Form nouns linked with the words on the left.

65 collect   Mark was very proud of his stamp ....

66 feed   They put the .... in the fridge.

67 know   The man's .... of sport was remarkable.

68 drive   James wanted to be a racing ....

69 warm   The .... from the fire made him sleepy.

70 see   The .... of the hills filled me with happiness.

71–80   Fill in the missing letters.

The old house stands at the c............r of the road.
It is almost c............d with ivy and there is
a b............ful garden all round it. Part of
the house is said to be four h............d years
old. The c............ns at the large windows are
made of heavy silk. There are fo............y rooms in the
house but they are not all used. The furn............
is old too, and most of it is very val............
Queen Elizabeth I is sup............ed to have slept in
one of the bedrooms but no one can be s............ that
this is true.

Underline two words in each line which have something in common with the word on the left.

81–82 **clock**   face   legs   ankles   hands   feet

83–84 **door**   book   handle   lesson   hinge   floor

85–86 **chair**   face   legs   hands   seat   top

87–88 **piano**   keys   locks   wheels   station   pedals

Every sixth word has been left out of this poem. Can you fill them in?

89–96

All this sea

And only ....

To watch it crawl

With .... and fall,

Over the sand

.... now I stand,

At break .... day

A castaway.

At dead .... night

And no starlight

I .... it roar

Towards the shore,

.... full of tears

I stop .... ears

I want a friend

Exile to end

97–100   Underline the adjectives in the following passage:

Cinderella slept in a cold garret, on a wretched, straw bed, while her step-sisters lay in fine rooms.

Total marks

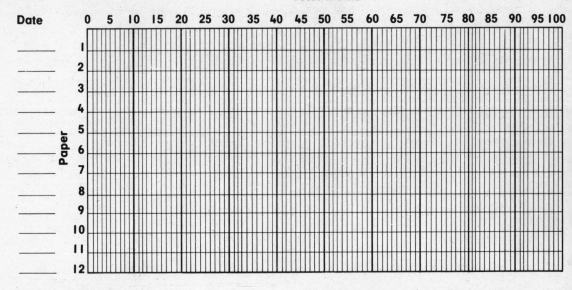

Thomas Nelson and Sons Ltd
Nelson House Mayfield Road
Walton-on-Thames Surrey
KT12 5PL UK

© **J M Bond 1965, 1983, 1988, 1994**

First published 1965
Revised edition 1983
Reprinted 1987, 1988
This fully revised edition 1994

I(T)P Thomas Nelson is an International
Thomson Publishing Company

I(T)P is used under licence

Pupil's book ISBN 0-17-424525-4
NPN 9 8 7 6 5 4 3
Answer book ISBN 0-17-424526-2
NPN 9 8 7 6 5 4 3 2

By the same author
First, Second, Third, Fourth and Further
Fourth Year Assessment Papers in Mathematics

First, Second, Third, Fourth and Further
Fourth Year Assessment Papers in English

First, Second, Third, Fourth and Further
Fourth Year Assessment Papers in Reasoning

Printed in Great Britain

Poems and extracts reproduced by kind permission of

Dolphin Concert Productions Ltd: Extract from **Oh I
wish I'd looked after me teeth** by Pam Ayres (Paper 1
Faber & Faber Ltd: **The Night Mail** from *Collected
poems* by W H Auden (Paper 10) and **Kenneth**
from *The Book of Comic Verse* by Wendy Cope
(Paper 2)
Oxford University Press; **Four o'clock** from
Tomorrow is my Love by Hal Summers
© Hal Summers 1978 (Paper 3)
Mrs A M Walsh: **Journey Home** from *The
Roundabout by the Sea* by John Walsh (Paper 6)

Cambridge University Press: **The School Year** and
A Week of Winter Weather by Wes Magee
(Papers 4 and 10)
George Allen & Unwin: Extract from *The Hobbit*
by J R R Tolkien (Paper 5)
William Heinemann Ltd: Extract from
101 Dalmations by Dodie Smith (Paper 7)

The publishers have made every attempt to trace
copyright holders of reprinted material, and
apologise for any errors or omissions.